SPORTS

This I-Spy book belongs to:

American Football

American Football was first played in such American universities as Harvard and Yale in the nineteenth century. Clearly, its origins lie in the British sports of football (soccer) and rugby football. How many players are there in an American Football team?

*I-Spy for **15***
Double with answer

Australian Football

This game is played on a pitch similar in shape to that of cricket. Goals are scored by kicking between goalposts, and the ball may be kicked, punched, or carried provided it is bounced every 10 m (33 ft).
*I-Spy for **20***

Baseball

Another ball game from the United States, Baseball gets its name from the four bases at the corners of the marked-out diamond shape which is the course around which the batter must run.

I-Spy for 20

Basketball

It is believed that a game similar to modern Basketball was played in the Central American country of Mexico as early as the tenth century. Basketball players must not move when they have the ball. True or False?

I-Spy for 15
Double with answer

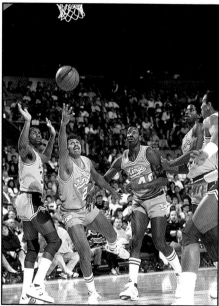

3

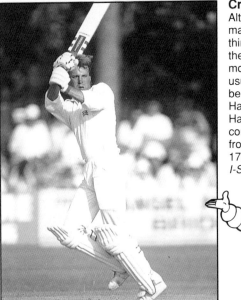

Cricket
Although its origins may go back to the thirteenth century, the home of the modern game is usually believed to be the village of Hambledon in Hampshire which controlled cricket from the late 1700s.
I-Spy for **10**

Football (Soccer)
The formal name for Soccer is Association Football. The game was played in England from as early as the fourteenth century but ball-kicking games existed at least 2000 years before that.
I-Spy for **5**

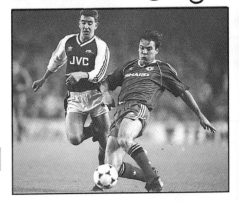

4

Golf

The 'official' home of Golf is the 'Royal and Ancient' Club at St Andrews on the east coast of Scotland, but a similar game may have been played in China several centuries before the birth of Christ. Mary Queen of Scots was a keen golfer. True or False?

*I-Spy for **10***
Double with answer

Handball

Team Handball is a goal-scoring game in which the players must not touch the ball with their feet or even the lower parts of their legs.
*I-Spy for **20***

5

Hockey

The game of Hockey may have originated in Ancient Egypt more than 4000 years ago. The name 'Hockey' was first used in the nineteenth century and may come from a old French word for what?

I-Spy for **15**
Double with answer

Hurling

Hurling is mainly an Irish game which is similar to hockey except that the ball may be carried on the stick as well as struck. It may even be hit with the hand or kicked.

I-Spy for **20**

Lacrosse

There are various legends to explain the origins of this game, but its basic object is to throw the ball into the opposing team's goal net using a stick with a mesh pouch at the end.

I-Spy for **15**

Netball

Although Netball is based on the American game of basketball, the rules of the modern game, which is played mainly by women, were drawn up in England at the beginning of this century.

I-Spy for **15**

Polo

Played on horseback, Polo is a team goal-scoring game in which the wooden ball is struck using a long-handled mallet. It has its origins in India and the word 'Polo' comes from a Kashmiri word meaning 'ball'.

I-Spy for **20**

Real Tennis

Originally played in medieval French monastery court-yards, Real Tennis is played in a walled court, and the players score points by aiming the ball so that it strikes particular areas on the walls. The other name of Real Tennis is ..... Tennis?

I-Spy for 25
Double with answer

Squash

The name of this game probably comes from the fact that, in the mid-1900s, boys of Harrow School would knock up in preparation for a game of rackets by hitting a 'squashy' or softer ball against a wall.
I-Spy for 15

Table Tennis

Legend has it that the game of Table Tennis began at Cambridge University when some students invented a game in which they hit champagne corks across a table using cigarette packets as bats.

I-Spy for **15**

Tennis

Lawn Tennis developed from Real Tennis, but the first club was not founded until the second half of the nineteenth century in Leamington Spa, England. The game is now played on various surfaces including tarmac, concrete, and clay.

I-Spy for **10**

Volleyball

Volleyball was invented in America at the end of the nineteenth century as a game more suited to those who found basketball too demanding. It may be played indoors or out and the idea is to prevent the ball from touching the ground.
I-Spy for **20**

Water Polo

Water Polo is a hand-ball, goal scoring game played in a swimming pool. Players may use only one hand to catch or dribble the ball and keep it for no more than 45 seconds before passing it.
I-Spy for **20**

Discus

Discus was one of
the four events
included in the
Ancient Greek
Olympian Games.
The Romans also
threw the discus
which was originally
a disc of metal or
stone and is
now of weighted
wood with a
metal rim.
*I-Spy for **15***

Hammer

Today's Hammer
consists of a 16-
pound (7.26-kg)
metal ball attached
to a grip by a wire.
The competitor uses
a spinning action
from inside a safety
cage to throw the
Hammer as far
as possible.
*I-Spy for **15***

High Jump

High Jump rules once disallowed athletes from leaping the bar head first. When this was relaxed, athletes used a technique which enabled them to achieve far greater heights.
I-Spy for 15

Hop, Step, Jump (Triple Jump)

Similar to the school sport of 'Hop, Skip, and Jump', the Triple Jump consists of a hop, a step, and a jump in succession. This event needs speed, strength, and technique.
I-Spy for 15

Javelin

Another of the Olympian events, Javelins were once thrown as weapons of war and it is not surprising that young men should have had their prowess tested by seeing who could throw the furthest. Today's event is for men and women.

I-Spy for 15

ong Jump

ike the Triple Jump, the ong Jump requires peed and explosive trength. Today's thletes achieve dis- ances approaching 9 m 29 ft). This is only half he distance that the merican big cat, the uma, can reach.

Spy for 15

Pole Vaulting

Pole Vaulting involves using a long, springy pole to propel the athlete over a high bar. Pole vaulters nowadays regularly achieve heights approaching 6 m (over 19 ft).

I-Spy for 15

Shot Put

Putting the Shot is the fourth Olympian throwing event. The men's shot, a metal ball, weighs 7.26 kg (16 lb) while the women's shot is considerably lighter.

I-Spy for 15

Hurdles

Hurdling is a sprinting event, over distances from 100 m to 400 m, in which the athletes leap the hurdles without breaking stride in their running. A competitor is disqualified for knocking over a hurdle. True or False?

I-Spy for 15
Double with answer

Marathon

Marathon takes its name from Marathon in Greece where the ancient Greeks won a famous victory over the Persians in 490 BC. The news was carried to Athens by a runner.
I-Spy for 15

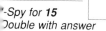

Middle-distance Running

One of the most famous middle distance runs is the 1-mile event. T[...] English athlete, Roger Bannister, was the first person to run a mile [...] less than 4 minutes in the year 1954. Today's top runners regularly run the distance in well under Bannister's time. Long-distance runni[...] looks very similar but the distances are greater. **Score an extra 5 points for each distance you spot.**

I-Spy for 15

Sprint

Sprint distances are from 60 m (indoors) up to 800 m (2 circuits of a 400 m track). Running competitions were organized in ancient Egypt almost 6000 years ago.

I-Spy for 15

Steeple Chase

The track event known as the 3000 m Steeple Chase is a gruelling event which takes the athletes over 3 ft high (0.91 m) fixed hurdles and 12 ft (3.66 m) water jumps with hurdles in front.

I-Spy for 15

Walking

Men's Walking events are set at distances of 20 km, 30 km, and 50 km. There is also a 2-hour walk. The women's distances are 5 km and 10 km. The difference between Walking and running is that on no occasion should both feet of the Walker leave the ground.

I-Spy for 15

Asymmetric Bars

This women's gymnastic event involves the competitor in carrying out graceful swinging and circling movements which must show good use of the two bars which are parallel but at different heights.

I-Spy for 15

Beam

The Balance Beam is 5 m (16 ft 3 in) long and only 10 cm (4 in) wide. Female gymnasts must carry out a linked series of turns, balances, jumps, and somersaults which require strength, grace, balance, and co-ordination.

I-Spy for 15

Floor

Individual men and women compete in Floor exercises although the men's event is not performed to music. Both events should combine acrobatic skills with strength and grace.

I-Spy for 15

Horse

There are two types of Horse: the Vaulting Horse, used by both men and women, and the Pommel Horse which has two rings or pommels set into the centre. **Score double if you spot both.**

I-Spy for 15

Parallel Bars

Unlike the asymmetric bars of the women's event, the men's Parallel Bars are at the same height. There is more emphasis on strength in the positions which must be held.

I-Spy for **15**

Rings

The Rings are suspended from the ceiling of the gymnasium by ropes. The male gymnast must carry out various swinging and holding exercises which require strength and grace.

I-Spy for **15**

Boxing

Boxing is thought to have originated as a sport some 3500 years ago in Ancient Greece. The amateur sport, in which the boxers wear vests as well as shorts and use large gloves, is set over three rounds. Professional boxers wear smaller gloves and no vests.
I-Spy for 15

Fencing

Obviously originating from ancient times when men fought battles with swords, the modern sport uses three kinds of weapon: the light foil, the slightly heavier épée, and the sabre which has cutting edges as well as points.
I-Spy for 20

Judo

Based on another Japanese martial art, Ju-jitsu, Judo was devised towards the end of the nineteenth century. It is one of the less violent and more sporting events. Experts learn to use an opponent's weight to overcome him or her.
I-Spy for 20

Karate

Originating from the Japanese island of Okinawa, in the sport of Karate, opponents aim to score 'hits' on each other using the knuckles of the first and middle fingers, the heel, side of foot, ball of foot, and instep.

I-Spy for 15

Sumo

The aim of each opponent in this 2000-year-old Japanese martial art is either to force the other out of the fighting circle or to bring him to the floor within it. Sumo wrestlers must be extremely strong, and body weight is also a considerable advantage.

I-Spy for 15

Wrestling

As its full name suggests, the modern sport of Greco-Roman style Wrestling has its origins in ancient Greece and was certainly one of the sports in the first Olympic Games in 708 BC.

I-Spy for 20
(half score for professional wrestling).

Abseiling

Perhaps not a sport in its own right, Abseiling involved descending a vertical surface, such as a cliff face, by sliding down a rope which passes under one thigh, across the body, and over the opposite shoulder. Modern abseilers use a device, called a descendeur, to slide down the rope.
I-Spy for 20

Parapenting

Similar to hang gliding, parapenting involves using a parachute to descend from a considerable height such as from a mountain top.
I-Spy for 20

Potholing

Otherwise known as Caving or Spelunking, Potholing is a modern sport although there are records to show that people did descend deep into cave systems as early as the eighteenth century.

I-Spy for **25**

Rock Climbing

With major advances in the quality of ropes, boots, and other equipment, rock climbing is a much safer sport than it once was but it is important to begin young. Who led the successful ascent of Mount Everest in 1953?

_____

I-Spy for **15**
Double with answer

BMX

The competitors race their bikes over specially built tracks which are surfaced with sand. There are downhill sections, climbs, banked curves, and various jumps. What do the initials 'BMX' stand for?

I-Spy for 15 Double with answer

Cycling

There are many different kinds of Cycle Racing including Hill Climbing, Pursuit, Time Trials, Sprint, and Stage Races such as the Tour de France. **Score an extra 5 points for each different type of cycling.**
I-Spy for 15

Cyclocross

This is cross-country cycle racing in which the competitors are faced with ploughed fields, gates, stiles, woods, and even rivers as well as roads. The cyclists are sometimes forced to carry their bikes.
I-Spy for 20

Mountain Biking

Mountain Bikes are often known as 'All Terrain Bicycles'. Although they are light in weight, they have strengthened frames, cantilever brakes, and wider wheels with fat, deep-treaded tyres.
I-Spy for 20

Billiards

The game of Billiards is played on a baize-covered table using only three balls, one cue ball for each of the opponents and a red ball. Points are scored by potting the red ball and by potting the opponent's cue ball by cannoning off the red ball.

I-Spy for **20**

Darts

Competition darts is usually played from a starting score of 501 which is reduced as the players score single, double, treble numbers or outers (25) and bulls (50). To win a player must finish on a double.

I-Spy for **10**

Snooker

It is thought that Snooker got its name from the slang word used in the army to describe a new cadet. The game was invented in the 1870s by officers in the British Army in India.
I-Spy for 10

Ten-pin Bowling

Ten-pin Bowling was developed in the United States. The ball is large and heavy with three finger holes for grip. Each player has two attempts to knock down the ten pins in each set.
I-Spy for 20

Canoeing

Canadian Canoes are broader in the beam than Kayaks. In the first the paddler kneels or squats and uses a single-bladed paddle, and in the Kayak, the paddler sits and uses a double-bladed paddle.

I-Spy for **20** *for each*

Coarse Fishing

Coarse Fishing or Angling involves using a rod, line and hook with various kinds of bait to catch freshwater fish which do not belong to the Salmon family.

I-Spy for **10**

Fly Fishing

In Fly Fishing or Game Fishing the person also uses a rod, hook, and line but the aim is to catch fish of the Salmon family using various kinds of fly-like lures. In Dry Fly Fishing, the 'fly' is designed to float. What is a 'Wet Fly' designed to do?

I-Spy for **20**
Double with answer

Rowing

Rowing sports also include 'Sculling' in which the rower uses two oars (strictly, the word Rowing should be used only to describe using one oar) The events include single sculls, pairs, fours, and eights where there is also a cox for steering the boat.
I-Spy for **15**

Archery

There are two main kinds of Archery using a Long Bow: Field Archery and Target Archery. Similarly there are two kinds using a Crossbow: Match Crossbow and Archery Crossbow. Crossbows use bolts rather than arrows.
*I-Spy for **20** for each*

Clay Pigeon Shooting

In this event the competitors use shotguns to shoot at a saucer-shaped clay target which is thrown in the air by a mechanical catapult-like device.
*I-Spy for **15***

Pistol Shooting

Pistols may be small bore, larger bore, or, as in the picture, air pistols. Targets may be stationary or, in rapid-fire events, the target may appear only for a short time.

I-Spy for 20

Rifle Shooting

There are two bores of rifle used using 'Standard' rifles or 'Free' rifles which have grips to help hold them steady. Targets are fired at from standing, kneeling, and lying positions.

I-Spy for 20

Ice Hockey
This game is played on ice by two teams of six players each and the aim of the game is to score by hitting a rubber disc, called a puck, into the opponent's goal which is defended by a goal keeper.
I-Spy for **15**

Ice Skating
Figure Skating may be performed by individual men and women as well as by pairs. Ice Dancing, which is shown here, is performed only by pairs.
I-Spy for **10**

Skiing
The word *Ski* is Norwegian, and simply means 'a stick of wood'. In Alpine Skiing, the racers ski down specially prepared snow slopes, while Nordic or Cross Country Skiers follow courses which are more natural.
I-Spy for 15

Ski Jumping
This sport probably has its origins in Norway in the eighteenth century. There are no official records for competitors in Ski Jumping because the heights of the ramps and the conditions may vary from place to place.
I-Spy for 15

Speed Skating

Speed Skaters race in pairs around a track on which they change lanes after each lap. They compete over as many as six races against the clock with the winner being decided on points.

I-Spy for 20

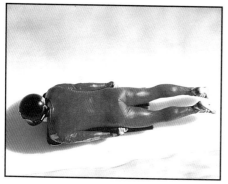

Toboggan

A Toboggan is a lightweight sled which may be ridden by individuals or by teams of two. Luge Toboggans are for one or two, but the competitors sit on them. In Skeleton Tobogganing, the solo rider lies face down.

I-Spy for 25

Dinghy Sailing

A Sailing Dinghy is a small, open sail boat usually with no permanent keel. There are many different kinds or 'Classes' and various competitions for each. The word 'dinghy' comes from an Indian word meaning 'boat'.

I-Spy for **10**

Diving

Competition Divers perform various somersaults, twists, and tucks of differing degrees of difficulty as they dive either from a springboard or a fixed highboard into a swimming pool.

I-Spy for **15**

Powerboat Racing

Powerboat Racing has its beginnings in an event for steam-powered boats that was first held off the coast of Scotland in 1827. Nowadays, there are various classes of Powerboats depending upon engine size, type of hull, etc.
I-Spy for 15

Surfing

The competitor stands or kneels on the specially designed surf board, and carries out various manoeuvres as he or she is carried towards the shore by the power of a breaking wave.
I-Spy for 15

Swimming

The four main strokes used in Swimming competitions are breaststroke, butterfly, backstroke, and freestyle (which nowadays is almost always the so-called 'crawl'). In Championship events, the distances range from 100 to 800 m.

I-Spy 5 for each stroke.

Synchronized Swimming

This is a sport for women only. It is carried out by solo competitors or by pairs or teams. The ballet-like routines are performed to music over set periods of time.
I-Spy for 15

Water Skiing

Water Skiing competitions usually involve the sportsmen and sportswomen performing a variety of acrobatic 'tricks' while being towed over a set course on one or two skis, or even barefoot.
I-Spy for 15

Wind Surfing

Competitors in Sailboard or Wind Surfing races compete either on triangular courses designed over deep water or on different kinds of courses set out nearer the shore in which surfing skills may also be needed.
I-Spy for **15**

Yachting

The word *Yacht* probably comes from a Danish word meaning 'hunting ship'. There are two main kinds of Yacht Racing: ocean racing and offshore racing around courses marked by buoys.
I-Spy for **20**

Drag Racing

Drag cars are specially designed, high-powered cars built to race from a standing start over $\frac{1}{4}$ mile (400 m) in the shortest possible time. The racers compete in pairs and the cars are brought to a halt with the aid of parachutes.

I-Spy for 20

Gliding

Gliders or Sailplanes may be flown in races against the clock over triangular courses which are marked out by suitable landmarks on the ground.

I-Spy for 20

Land Yachting
Sometimes known as Sand Yachts, these sail-powered, wheeled machines may carry a crew of up to 4 people and race over sandy beaches, deserts, or on roads and old runways.
I-Spy for **25**

Motor Racing
There are various kinds of Motor Racing, but the best known is probably the so-called Formula 1 event in which drivers and cars up to 3 litres compete on various tracks around the world for the Grand Prix championship.
I-Spy for **10**

Motorcycle Racing

In road racing riders on machines between 50 cc and 750 cc compete on specially built circuits or, in the case of the Isle of Man TT, on closed-off public roads around the island. What do the initials 'TT' stand for?

*I-Spy for **10***
Double with answer

Moto X

This event was once better known as Motorcycle Scrambling. Machines from 125 to 1000 cc are used to race over a cross-country track.
*I-Spy for **15***

Rallying
Motor Car rallies are held partly on public roads and the competitors must follow a set course between check-points. They must arrive at any given check point before a set time or they incur penalty points.
I-Spy for 15

Roller Skating
Most of the events which are performed in Ice Skating, such as Figures, Dancing, and Speed Skating may also be carried out on Roller Skates.
I-Spy for 20

43

Skate Boarding

Skateboarders use either their own energy or the energy developed by competing in a bowl-shaped area to perform various acrobatic 'tricks' sometimes to music.

*I-Spy for **20***

Speedway

The best-known type of Speedway event is raced between four competitors riding 500 cc motorcycles over four laps of an oval-shaped dirt or shale track.

*I-Spy for **15***

Driving

Driving events, using a four-wheeled carriage and four horses, may involve trotting or walking marathons as well as competing by driving around a course in which various obstacles, such as bridges and turns, have been set out.
I-Spy for 20

Greyhound Racing

In this event, Greyhounds are released from starting traps and chase an electrically powered 'hare' around a circuit over distances up to 880 yards (805 m).
I-Spy for 15

Horse Racing

There are three main kinds of Horse Racing: Flat Racing, where there are no obstacles, Hurdles, and Steeple Chasing where there is a mixture of hurdles, fences, ditches, and water jumps.

I-Spy 10 for each kind

Horse Trials

Horse Trials or Three-day Events include steeple-chases over fixed fences, cross-country competitions, show jumping, and steeple chases over brush fences.

I-Spy for 15

Show Jumping

A great variety of fences, including water jumps, may be set out over indoor or outdoor courses which usually involve competitions against the clock with penalty points or 'faults' given for refusals or for knocking down all or part of the jump.
I-Spy for **15**

Trotting

In this event, one horse pulls a lightweight, two-wheeled cart called a sulky or a bike. The horse moves front left leg and rear right together and so on. A similar event, called Pacing, has the horse moving front left and rear left together.
I-Spy for **20**

INDEX

Answers

American Football: 11.
Basketball: False.
Golf: True.
Hurdles: False.
Royal Tennis: Real Tennis.
Hockey: A shepherd's crook.
BMX: Bicycle Moto Cross
Fly Fishing: Sink.
Rock Climbing: Edmund Hillary.
Motor Cycle Racing: Tourist Trophy.

© I-Spy Limited 1991

ISBN (paperback) 1 85671 021 1
ISBN (hard cover) 1 85671 022 X

Michelin Tyre Public Limited Company
Davy House, Lyon Road, Harrow, Middlesex HA1 2DQ

MICHELIN and the Michelin Man are Registered Trademarks of Michelin

A CIP record for this title is available from the British Library.

Edited and designed by Curtis Garratt Limited, The Old Vicarage, Horton cum Studley, Oxford OX9 1BT

The Publisher gratefully acknowledges the contribution of Allsport who provided all the photographs in this I-Spy book. Cover photograph: Alex Williams.

Colour reproduction by Norwich Litho Services Limited.

Printed in Spain.